LITTLE TERRY TIDDLEMOUSE

AND HIS COUNTRYSIDE FRIENDS

His Countryside Friends

Little Terry Tiddlemouse with brothers Snitch and Snatch

Together live quite happily in their house that's made of thatch.

They love to nibble at the corn that grows in fields nearby

But shake and shudder in their coats when the harvester goes by.

They like to play at Tig and Run and catch each other's tails

They also play at Climb the Wall with the slugs and snails.

When Mollie Mole plays Hide and Seek, she always wins the game

So Terry, Snitch and Snatch and Vole don't enjoy it quite the same.

Their favourite friend is Cousin Vole who invites them in for tea

He also asks Sir Cyril Squirrel whose home's the old oak tree.

Fergus Frog, another friend, just loves to leap about

He's much too busy to use a cup so drinks it from the spout.

Hector Hog sniffs and snorts looking for his dinner

Terry thinks, without his spines, Hector would look thinner.

Mistress Mog is on the prowl, she hunts for birds and mice,

Which Snitch and Snatch and Terry think a most unwelcome vice.

There was a time when sheepdog Jim could also be unkind

But now he's old and going blind, so Terry doesn't mind.

He and brothers Snitch and Snatch even have a try

To touch the end of old Jim's tail - as if they were a fly!

Once the day has come and gone, and night puts on her cloak

Each creature finds their nest, of thatch or ditch or oak.

Then the little mice sleep sound, all cuddled in a huddle

You can't tell Terry from Snitch or Snatch, they're just a mousey muddle.

Little Terry Tiddlemouse
goes camping

Little Terry Tiddlemouse with brothers Snitch and Snatch

Together live quite happily in their house that's made of thatch.

One day they all went camping along the river's edge,

They made a tent for shelter against a leafy hedge.

Terry took his fishing rod, he hoped to catch a fish,

While Snitch and Snatch munched on corn, their very favourite dish.

The water glittered merrily and beckoned them to come,

The brothers went out sailing to have a little fun.

Their yacht was half a date-box, a leaf became their sail,

They couldn't find a rudder so Terry used his tail.

Exploring was exciting, there was so much to see,

A water rat peeped out at them - an owl peered from a tree.

The lily pads were covered, by frogs both large and small,

And Mister Toad croaked out "hello" from his reed-bed hall.

A dragonfly swooped down on them to greet them on their way,

While bumblebees buzzed busily to pass the time of day.

Their outing down the river was a mouse's tip-top treat,

They used a little water to sponge their snouts and feet.

They saw a dark brown trout at the bottom of a pool

But Terry had forgot his rod - oh dear he was a fool!

Terry felt quite hungry so he turned the boat around,

They sailed back up the river till they reached their camping ground.

They had no fish to eat and the sun was setting low,

So Terry led them home again, with Snitch and Snatch in tow.

Now the day had ended and darkness called them in

They ate a meal of sweet corn gnawed straight from the tin.

Tiredness overtook them, their thoughts were in a fuddle,

So Snitch and Snatch and Terry slept in their happy mousey muddle.

Published by Ailsapress 2016
Port Charlotte Isle of Islay PA48 7TS
www. ailsapress.com

ISBN 978-0-9555656-9-4

Text © Joan Porter 2016   Illustrations © Jessica Excell 2016

Also by Joan Porter and Jessica Excell
'LITTLE TERRY TIDDLEMOUSE AND TIME FOR TEA AND DRESSING UP'

Printed by Grafistar BV Netherlands
www. grafistar.nl